Basic Skill

SPELLING

for 7 – 8 year olds

Contents

Unit 1	Magic e words 1	
Unit 2	Magic e words 2	
Unit 3	Words with oa and ou	
Unit 4	Words with ow	
Unit 5	Words with wh and th	
Unit 6	Words with ea	

Progress check 1

Unit 7	Words with oy and oi	
Unit 8	Compound words	
Unit 9	Words with y	
Unit 10	Words with oo	
Unit 11	Words with ce and ge	
Unit 12	Words with igh	

Progress check 2

Answers

Record sheet

Louis Fidge

Magic e words 1

When you add an **e** to the end of some short words, the sound of the vowel in the middle of the word can change.

cap   cape

What a difference the magic **e** makes.

 TRY THESE

1. Write the magic **e** words you make.

hat	+ e =	hate
mad	+ e =	
can	+ e =	
rid	+ e =	
pip	+ e =	
win	+ e =	
rob	+ e =	
to	+ e =	

Write these words without the magic **e**.

tape	– e =	tap
mate	– e =	
cape	– e =	
hide	– e =	
pine	– e =	
shine	– e =	
rode	– e =	
mope	– e =	

MORE PRACTICE

2. Choose the correct word for each picture.

hat hate	rid ride	mop mope	tub tube
			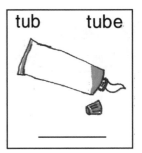
<u>hat</u>	_____	_____	_____

3. Write these sentences again. Correct the underlined words.

I <u>cane</u> rid my bike.
<u>I can ride my bike.</u>

I drank water from the <u>tape.</u>
_____

I can <u>wine</u> the race.

_____

I <u>hop</u> you get well soon.

_____

 CHECK UP

4. Find and circle the magic **e** words.

a b c d h (m i l e) f g j

n m h o p e n t y z x w

g f d s p i n e y t y u p

s h a p e q w e r t y u k

d c u b e z a q m x n d

d x v b c z b o n e x r l

Magic e words 2

 **FOCUS**

The vowel in the middle of magic **e** words says its name, not its sound.

| tape | wine | rope | tube |

TRY THESE

1. Write the words you can make.

Change the **c** in cake to **m, r, l, t, b.**

make _____ _____ _____ _____

Change the **s** in same to **g, f, n, t, c.**

_____ _____ _____ _____ _____

2. Join up the rhyming words.   Write the words.

side   smile ⟶ _____

pile   rise   ⟶ _____

time   wide   ⟶ side   wide

wise   five   ⟶ _____

dive   chime ⟶ _____

Unit 2

MORE PRACTICE

3. Choose the right word for each picture.

| mole | bone | joke | hose | doze |

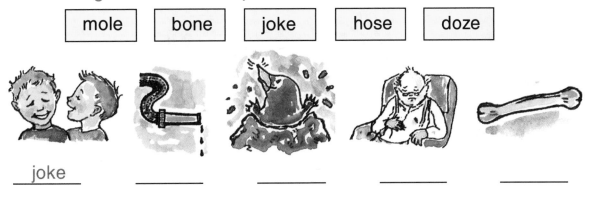

__joke__   _____   _____   _____   _____

4. Use the words above to answer these:

A dog eats this. __bone__   You tell this. _____

I dig a hole. _____   A baby does this. _____

Water comes from this. _____

 CHECK UP

5. Choose the correct word for each picture.

| cub cube | plum plume | cut cute |

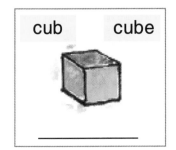      

_____   _____   _____

Unit 2

Words with oa and ou

FOCUS

The patterns **oa** and **ou** never come at the end of a word.

load   loud   coach   couch

TRY THESE

1. Find the pairs of words in the goal.

boat   moan   croak
toad   coast
coat   soak   groan
road   toast

Write the words.

boat	coat

2. Find and circle the words with the same letter pattern.

shout	loud	house	hound	about
proud	couch	cloud	mouth	count
pound	sound	south	spout	house
count	scout	crouch	amount	proud
south	mouse	cloud	bound	mouth
couch	crouch	about	count	ground

Unit 3

MORE PRACTICE

3. Complete each word with either **oa** or **ou**.

t o a d
toad

cl _ _ d
_____

m _ _ se
_____

m _ _ th
_____

h _ _ nd
_____

g _ _ l
_____

cl _ _ k
_____

l _ _ f
_____

4. Draw:

a coat on the goat

a mouse in the house

 CHECK UP

5. Fill the cloud with **ou** words. Fill the boat with **oa** words.

Words with ow

See butterfly book p 15

FOCUS

Some letter patterns look the same but have different sounds.

bow

bow

TRY THESE

1. Make the **ow** words in the flower.

t_ _n   g_ _n   h_ _l   _ _l   ow   cl_ _n   cow

Write the word that means:

an animal that gives milk	cow
where people live	_____
a bird	_____
something ladies wear	_____
a funny person	_____
a noise wolves make	_____

2. Make the **ow** words in the window.

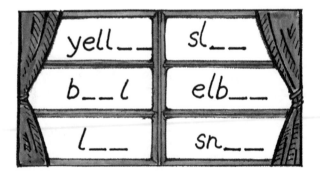

yell_ _   sl_ _   b_ _l   elb_ _   l_ _   sn_ _

Write the word that means:

not high	_____
not fast	_____
a container	_____
frozen rain	_____
part of your arm	_____
a colour	_____

Unit 4

MORE PRACTICE

3. Write the ow words that sound like the ow in snow, in the snowman.
   Write the ow words that sound like the ow in clown, in the clown.

low	now	mow	how	brown	crow
slow	shown	cow	owl	crown	blow

 CHECK UP

4. Unscramble the letters. Write the words.

wco	wol	obwl	nswo	erowt	owmre

cow _____ _____ _____ _____ _____

Words with wh and th

You have to put your lips together **when** you **wh**istle.

You have to put your tongue between your tee**th** when you say **th**anks.

TRY THESE

1. Finish these words.

t h i n

——i n k

——u m b s

——u n d e r

——a n k s

——u m p

——e m

Write the words with 4 letters.

Write the words with 5 letters.

Write the words with 6 letters.

Write the word with 7 letters.

2. Write the correct word under each picture.

| path | bath | moth | teeth |

_____ _____ _____ _____

Unit 5

MORE PRACTICE

3. Make the words.

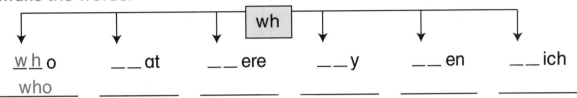

w h o   __ at   __ ere   __ y   __ en   __ ich

who   _____   _____   _____   _____   _____

4. Write each word under the correct picture.

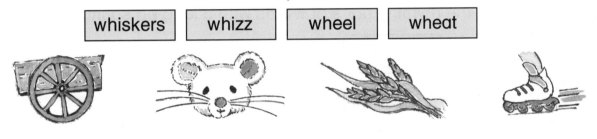

| whiskers | whizz | wheel | wheat |

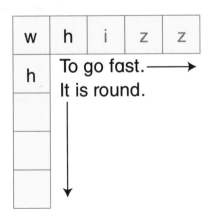

wheel _____   _____   _____   _____

 CHECK UP

5. Complete these crosswords.

w	h	i	z	z
h	To go fast. →			
	It is round.			

w	h					
h	Cats have them. →					
	Bread is made from it.					

Words with ea

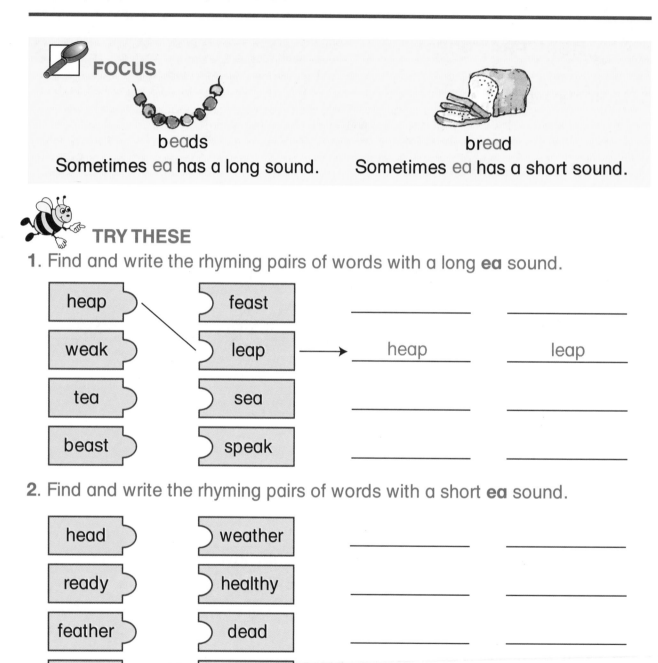

beads
Sometimes ea has a long sound.

bread
Sometimes ea has a short sound.

TRY THESE

1. Find and write the rhyming pairs of words with a long **ea** sound.

heap	feast	_____	_____
weak	leap	⟶ heap	leap
tea	sea	_____	_____
beast	speak	_____	_____

2. Find and write the rhyming pairs of words with a short **ea** sound.

head	weather	_____	_____
ready	healthy	_____	_____
feather	dead	_____	_____
wealthy	steady	_____	_____

Unit 6

MORE PRACTICE

3. Find and circle the **ea** in these words.

n(ea)t	heavy	meadow	steam	jealous	peach
leather	beast	cream	deaf	pleasant	speak

4. Write the words in the correct boxes.

Words with a short **ea** sound.	Words with a long **ea** sound.
heavy	neat

5. Use some of the words above to answer these:

Not light ___heavy___   Unable to hear _____

Tidy _____   A fruit _____

A field _____   Made from milk _____

 **CHECK UP**

6. In each word:

Put ∨ above the **ea** if it is short. Put — above the **ea** if it is long.

brĕad	bēat	heap	thread	feast	eagle
sweat	tread	weak	teach	weather	already

1. Add a magic **e** to these words:

rob__   tub__   cap__   win__

Now write each **magic e** word under the correct picture.

_____   _____   _____   _____

2. Join the rhyming words.   Write the words.

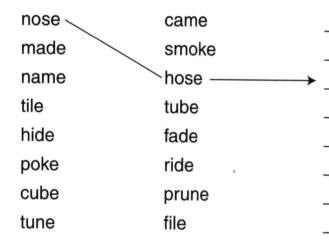

_____	_____
_____	_____
nose	hose
_____	_____
_____	_____
_____	_____
_____	_____
_____	_____

3. Finish each word with **oa** or **ou**.

sh__ __t   c__ __ __t   c__ __ __st   h__ __ __se

gr__ __ __n   cl__ __ __d   m__ __ __th   s__ __ __k

s__ __ __nd   r__ __ __d

4. If the **ow** in the word sounds like the **ow** in c**ow** colour the word **red**.
   If the **ow** in the word sounds like the **ow** in sn**ow** colour the word **blue**.

| how | low | mow | now | owl |

| grow | flow | brown | growl | yellow |

5. Finish each word with **wh** or th.
   Colour the **wh** bricks red. Colour the th bricks yellow.

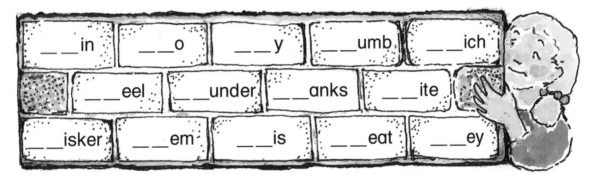

| _ _ in | _ _ o | _ _ _ y | _ _ _ umb | _ _ _ ich |

| _ _ _ eel | _ _ _ under | _ _ _ anks | _ _ _ ite |

| _ _ isker | _ _ _ em | _ _ _ is | _ _ _ eat | _ _ _ ey |

6. Join up the words that sound alike.

beak | break | steak
threat
speak
plead
sweat | head | tread | feast
beast | bead |

Progress check 1

Words with oy and oi

 **FOCUS**

The letter patterns **oy** and **oi** both sound the same.

boy

The **oy** often comes at the end of words.

boil

The **oi** often comes in the middle of words.

 TRY THESE

1. Colour the **oy** words **red**. Colour the **oi** words **blue**.

boy	boil	coin	joy	toy	hoist
enjoy	choice	annoy	noise	employ	
coil	foil	destroy	spoil	point	avoid

2. Now write the words in the correct boxes.

oy words	oi words
boy	boil

MORE PRACTICE

3. Write the correct words under the pictures.

| coin | toy | point | destroy |

_____ _____ _____ _____

4. Use the best word to fill in each space.

| point | enjoy | joy | boil | toy | voice | boy |

I __ __ __ __ __ swimming.

You can __ __ __ __ eggs in water.

The arrow had a sharp __ __ __ __ __ .

The __ __ __ got a lot of __ __ __ from his new __ __ __ .

The singer had a lovely __ __ __ __ __ .

✓ CHECK UP

5. Complete each word with either **oi** or **oy**.

sp__ __ l   m__ __ st   j__ __   t__ __   n__ __ sy   empl__ __

ann__ __   j__ __ nt   ch__ __ ce   destr__ __   b__ __   av__ __ d

Compound words

FOCUS

butter   **+**   **fly**   **=**   **butterfly**

Sometimes we can join two small words together to make a longer word.

TRY THESE

1. Do these picture sums to make some longer words.

 + **=** _____ buttercup _____

 + **=** _____

 + **=** _____

 + **=** _____

 + **=** _____

Unit 8

MORE PRACTICE

2. Match up the beginnings and endings to make some longer words.

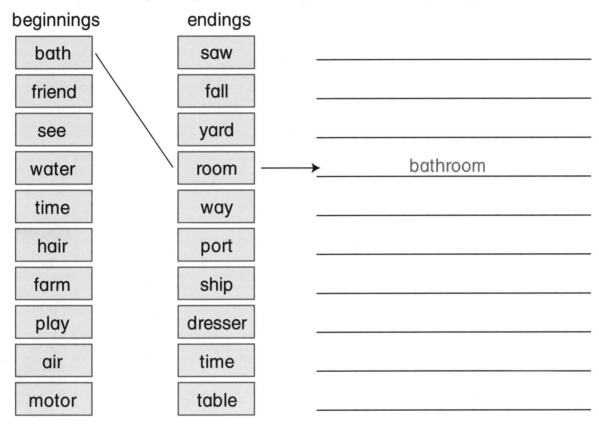

beginnings	endings
bath	saw
friend	fall
see	yard
water	room → _____ bathroom _____
time	way
hair	port
farm	ship
play	dresser
air	time
motor	table

_____
_____
_____
_____
_____
_____
_____

✓ CHECK UP

3. Add a small word in each gap.

out_____   after_____   my_____   when_____

every_____   some_____   sea_____   foot_____

under_____   round_____   grand_____   over_____

Words with y

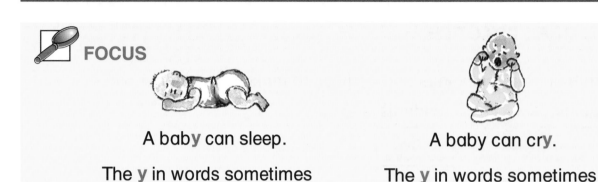

FOCUS

A baby can sleep.

The **y** in words sometimes sounds like **ee** (as in bab**y**).

A baby can cry.

The **y** in words sometimes sounds like **ie** (as in cr**y**).

TRY THESE

1. Make these words. The **y** sounds like **ee**.

Write them and see!

y

bab__   lad__   bod__   tin__   cop__   hand__

Now make these words. The **y** sounds like **ie**.

Why not have a try?

y

b__   m__   cr__   tr__   fl__   wh__

2. Write the **y** words that sound like **ee** in the bee.
   Write the **y** words that sound like **ie** in the fly.

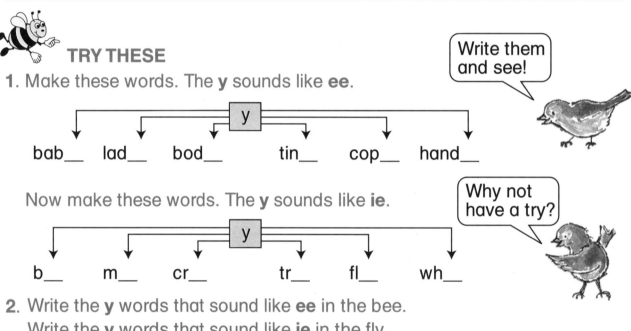

baby

by

MORE PRACTICE

3. What is the weather like? Write the words under the pictures.

| foggy | sunny | rainy | snowy |

_____ _____ _____ _____

4. Match the words with their meanings.

| dry | funny | penny | reply | supply | poppy |

To answer _____   The opposite of wet _____

To provide _____   A coin _____

A flower _____   Amusing _____

✔ CHECK UP

5. Colour **red** the words in which the **y** sounds like **ee**.
Colour **blue** the words in which the **y** sounds like **ie**.

lumpy   risky   fry   empty   multiply   apply   happy   rely   tiny   shy

Words with oo

FOCUS
Always look carefully at words to try to find common letter patterns.

The crook took some books.

TRY THESE

1.

Finish the words with ook.	Write the words.	Finish the words with ood.	Write the words.
c _ _ _ _	cook	h _ _ _ _	
b _ _ _ _		w _ _ _ _	
h _ _ _ _		g _ _ _ _	
r _ _ _ _		st _ _ _ _	

2. Finish the words below.

a c _ _ _ _ ery b _ _ _ _

Red Riding H _ _ _ _ in the w _ _ _ _

MORE PRACTICE

3. Read this story. Underline all the **oo** words in it.

One day I took my friend to look for
birds in the woods. We wore our coats
with hoods. When we stood still we
saw many big black rooks near the
brook. Suddenly my foot slipped.
I fell into the water and shook
with cold.

ook words	

ood words	

oot word	

 CHECK UP

4. The last letter of each word is wrong.
Rewrite each word and end it with either **k**, **t** or **d**.

lood ___look___   fook _____   broot_____   gook_____

sood _____   blook_____   bood_____   stoot_____

cood_____   wook _____   croot_____   rood _____

Words with ce and ge

a nice ice lolly

a cage

Whenever **c** is followed by **e** it sounds like **s**.

Whenever **g** is followed by **e** it sounds like **j**.

 **TRY THESE**

1. Write the words.

ice	ace	age
n <u>i</u> <u>c</u> <u>e</u>	f __ __ __	r __ __ __
sl __ __ __	pl __ __ __	c __ __ __
tw __ __ __	sp __ __ __	p __ __ __

2. Use each of the words above to complete the sentences.

a. I like a n __ __ __ sl __ __ __ of cake.

b. The parrot was in a c __ __ __.

c. The rocket flew into sp __ __ __.

d. I fell over tw __ __ __ and cut my f __ __ __.

e. When I am angry I get into a r __ __ __.

f. There was a p __ __ __ missing from my book.

g. The playground is a noisy pl __ __ __.

MORE PRACTICE

3. Write the correct word under each picture.

fence	orange	hinge	dance

_____ _____ _____ _____

4. Underline the **nce** words in **green** and the **nge** words in **blue**.

chance	strange	glance	pence	fringe
plunge	mince	singe	prince	cringe

Now write the words in two sets:

nce words	nge words

 CHECK UP

5. These words are jumbled up. Write them correctly.

agce   eic   cande   granoe

_____ _____ _____ _____

Words with igh

a bright light

When the letters **igh** come together you do not pronounce the **gh**.

TRY THESE

1. Make these words.

h	→ igh →	high
s	→ igh →	_____
th	→ igh →	_____
r	→ ight →	_____
s	→ ight →	_____
m	→ ight →	_____
br	→ ight →	_____
fr	→ ight →	_____
sl	→ ight →	_____
fl	→ ight →	_____

MORE PRACTICE

2. Circle all the **igh** words in this story.

The princess gave a deep sigh. She had been locked up in a high tower by the wicked queen. She was frightened. There was not much light at night. Just then there was sound right outside. The princess looked out. What a sight met her eyes! A handsome prince was there on a white horse. He threw up a rope with all his might. The princess held on tight as she climbed down. She was free at last!

Make a list of all the **igh** words you found.

....

....

....

....

....

 CHECK UP

3. Find and circle the **igh** words.

☆ a b c d h m i g h t f g j   ☆ n m s i g h n t y z x w

☆ g f n i g h t x w y t y u p   ☆ s f r i g h t q w e r t y u

☆ d b r i g h t a q m x n d   ☆ d x v b c z h i g h x r l

Progress check 2

1. Complete each word with either **oy** or **oi**.

b __ __   b __ __ l   c __ __ n   destr __ __

2. Now write the correct word under each picture.

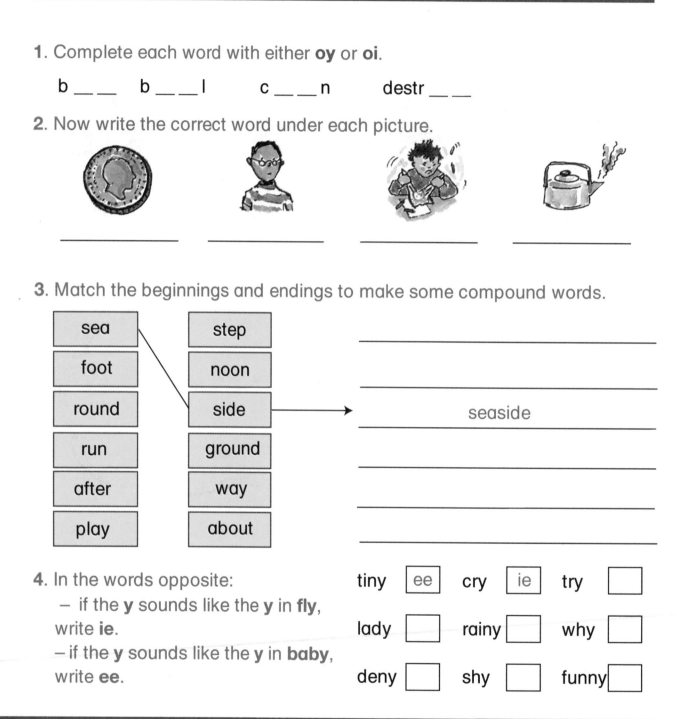

_____   _____   _____   _____

3. Match the beginnings and endings to make some compound words.

sea		step
foot		noon
round		side
run		ground
after		way
play		about

_____

_____

seaside

_____

_____

_____

4. In the words opposite:
 – if the **y** sounds like the **y** in **fly**, write **ie**.
 – if the **y** sounds like the **y** in **baby**, write **ee**.

tiny ee   cry ie   try ☐

lady ☐   rainy ☐   why ☐

deny ☐   shy ☐   funny ☐

5. Join the words that contain the same letter patterns.

6. Finish each word with **ce** or **ge**.
Colour the **ce** bricks **red**. Colour the **ge** bricks yellow.

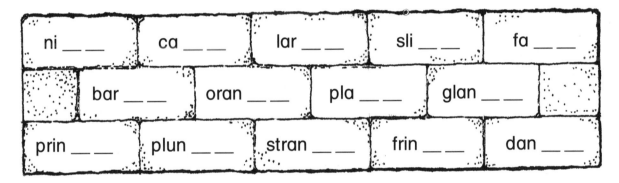

ni _ _ _   ca _ _ _   lar _ _ _   sli _ _ _   fa _ _ _

bar _ _ _   oran _ _ _   pla _ _ _   glan _ _ _

prin _ _ _   plun _ _ _   stran _ _ _   frin _ _ _   dan _ _ _

7. These words all sound the same.
Join the words with the same letter patterns.

try	pie	buy	high
sigh	guy	die	why

8. Now write four words that contain the letter pattern **ight**.

_____   _____   _____   _____

Answers

Unit 1

1. hate   tap
   made   mat
   cane   cap
   ride   hid
   pipe   pin
   wine   shin
   robe   rod
   toe   mop
2. hat   ride   mop   tube
3. I can ride my bike.
   I drank water from the tap.
   I can win the race.
   I hope you get well soon.
4. mile   hope
   pine   shape
   cube   bone

Unit 2

1. make,   rake,   lake,   take,
   bake,   game,   fame,   name,
   tame,   came
2. pile - smile
   wise - rise
   side - wide
   dive - five
   time - chime
3. joke   hose   mole   doze
   bone
4. bone   joke   mole   doze
   hose
5. cube,   plume,   cut

Unit 3

1. boat - coat   toad - road
   soak - croak   coast - toast
   moan - groan
2. shout - about   proud - cloud
   pound - sound   count - amount
   south - mouth   couch - crouch
3. toad   cloud   mouse   mouth
   hound   goal   cloak   loaf

4. See drawing.
5. Many possible answers.

Unit 4

1. cow,   town,   owl,   gown,
   clown,   howl
2. low,   slow,   bowl,   snow,
   elbow,   yellow
3. In snowman-
   low,   mow,   crow,   slow,
   shown,   blow
   In clown -
   now,   how,   brown,   cow,
   owl,   crown
4. cow,   owl,   bowl,   snow,
   tower,   mower

Unit 5

1. 4 letter words: thin,   them
   5 letter words: think,   thump
   6 letter words: thumbs, thanks
   7 letter word: thunder
2. mouth   bath   moth   path
3. who   what   where   why
   when   which
4. wheel   whiskers
   wheat   whizz
5. across: whizz
   down: wheel
   across: whiskers
   down: wheat

Unit 6

1. beast - feast   heap - leap
   tea - sea   weak - speak
2. feather - weather
   wealthy - healthy
   head - dead
   ready - steady
3. neat,   heavy,   meadow,
   steam,   jealous,   peach,

leather,   beast,   cream,   deaf,
pleasant,   speak
4. short ea words:
   heavy,   meadow, jealous,
   leather,   deaf,   pleasant
   long ea words:
   neat,   steam,   peach,
   beast,   cream,   speak
5. heavy   deaf   neat   peach
   meadow cream
6. short ea:
   bread,   thread,   sweat,   tread,
   weather, already
   long ea:
   beat,   heap,   feast,   eagle,
   weak,   teach

Progress check 1

1. robe   tube   cape   wine
   cape   robe   wine   tube
2. name - came   poke - smoke
   nose - hose   cube - tube
   made - fade   hide - ride
   tune - prune   tile - file
3. shout   coat   coast   house
   groan   cloud   mouth   soak
   sound   road
4. red:
   how   now   owl
   brown   growl
   blue:
   low   mow   grow   flow
   yellow
5. wh words:
   who,   why,   which,   wheel,
   white,   whisker, wheat
   th words:
   thin,   thumb,   thunder, thanks,
   them,   this,   they
6. beak - speak   break - steak
   sweat - threat   head - tread
   beast - feast   bead - plead

Unit 7

1
+2. oy/red words:
boy, joy, toy, enjoy, annoy, employ, destroy
oi/blue words:
boil, coin, hoist, choice, noise, coil, foil, spoil, point, avoid

3. toy point coin destroy

4. enjoy, boil, point, boy, joy, toy, voice, join

5. spoil, moist, joy, toy, noisy, employ, annoy, joint choice, destroy, boy, avoid

Unit 8

1. buttercup snowman
ladybird keyhole
sheepdog

2. seesaw waterfall
farmyard bathroom
motorway airport
friendship hairdresser
playtime timetable

3. Many possible answers.

Unit 9

1. baby, lady, body, tiny, copy, handy
by, my, cry, try, fly, why

2. ee words in bee:
baby, lady, body, tiny, copy, handy
ie words in fly:
by, my, cry, try, fly, why

3. rainy foggy snowy sunny

4. reply dry supply penny
poppy funny

5. red ee words:
lumpy, risky, empty, happy, tiny
blue ie words:
fry, multiply, apply, rely, shy

Unit 10

1. cook, book, hook, rook
hood, wood, good, stood

2. a cookery book
Red Riding Hood in the wood

3. ook words:
took, rooks, brook, shook
ood words:
woods, hoods, stood
oot word:
foot

4. look food brook good
soot blood book stood
cook wood crook
rook (or root)

Unit 11

1. nice face rage slice
place cage twice space
page

2. a. nice, slice e. rage
b. cage f. page
c. space g. place
d. twice, face

3. orange dance fence hinge

4. green nce words:
chance, glance, pence, mince, prince
blue nge words:
strange, fringe, plunge, singe, cringe

5. cage ice dance orange

Unit 12

1. high, sigh, thigh, right, sight, might, bright, fright, slight, flight

2. sigh, high, frightened, light, night, right, sight, might, tight

3. might sight night fright bright high

Progress check 2

1. boy boil coin destroy
2. coin boy destroy boil
3. footstep, afternoon, seaside, playground, runway, roundabout
4. tiny (ee) cry (ie)
try (ie) lady (ee)
rainy (ee) why (ie)
deny (ie) shy (ie)
funny (ee)
5. cook - book - took
hood - good - stood - wood
foot - soot - sooty
6. red ce words:
nice, slice, face, place, glance, prince, dance
yellow ge words:
cage, large, barge, orange, plunge, strange, fringe
7. try - why, pie - die,
buy - guy, sigh - high
8. Many possible answers.

Record sheet

How easy did you find it?

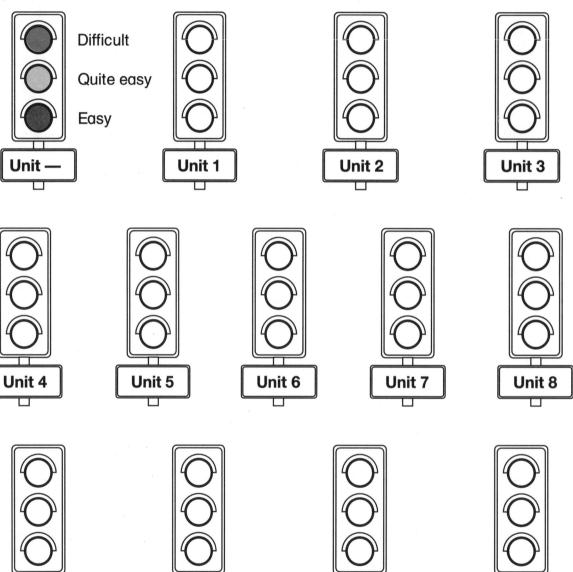

Difficult

Quite easy

Easy

Unit —

Unit 1

Unit 2

Unit 3

Unit 4

Unit 5

Unit 6

Unit 7

Unit 8

Unit 9

Unit 10

Unit 11

Unit 12

Record sheet